D1092696

THIS BOOK BELONGS TO:

CONTACT INFORMATION

NAME:	
ADDRESS:	
PHONE:	

START / END DATES

/   /   TO   /   /

MY SESSION

DATE		WEEK		SESSION	
BELT		INSTRUCTOR			

MY GOALS OF THE DAY

- ☐
- ☐
- ☐
- ☐
- ☐

TRAINING PARTNERS

☐	☐
☐	☐
☐	☐

TECHNIQUES COVERED	WARM UP / DRILLS

WHAT I HAVE LEARNED	POINTS FOR IMPROVEMENT

NOTES

SKILLS COMPLETED
WRITE DOWN THE SKILLS YOU WORKED ON AND DEVELOPED DURING YOUR CLASS

SKILLS TO IMPROVE
WRITE DOWN AREAS THAT YOU CAN IMPROVE ON FOR YOUR NEXT TRAINING SESSION

INSTRUCTOR FEEDBACK
WRITE DOWN IF YOUR INSTRUCTOR HAS A SKILL, TECHNIQUE, OR COMBINATION FOR YOU TO FOCUS ON

EXTRA NOTES
DO YOU HAVE EXTRA NOTES OR THOUGHTS YOU WOULD LIKE TO WRITE DOWN?

JOURNAL

JOURNAL

MY SESSION

DATE		WEEK		SESSION	
BELT		INSTRUCTOR			

MY GOALS OF THE DAY

- ☐
- ☐
- ☐
- ☐
- ☐

TRAINING PARTNERS

☐	☐
☐	☐
☐	☐

TECHNIQUES COVERED	WARM UP / DRILLS

WHAT I HAVE LEARNED	POINTS FOR IMPROVEMENT

NOTES

SKILLS COMPLETED
WRITE DOWN THE SKILLS YOU WORKED ON AND DEVELOPED DURING YOUR CLASS

SKILLS TO IMPROVE
WRITE DOWN AREAS THAT YOU CAN IMPROVE ON FOR YOUR NEXT TRAINING SESSION

INSTRUCTOR FEEDBACK
WRITE DOWN IF YOUR INSTRUCTOR HAS A SKILL, TECHNIQUE, OR COMBINATION FOR YOU TO FOCUS ON

EXTRA NOTES
DO YOU HAVE EXTRA NOTES OR THOUGHTS YOU WOULD LIKE TO WRITE DOWN?

JOURNAL

JOURNAL

MY SESSION

DATE		WEEK		SESSION	
BELT		INSTRUCTOR			

MY GOALS OF THE DAY

☐

☐

☐

☐

☐

TRAINING PARTNERS

☐	☐
☐	☐
☐	☐

TECHNIQUES COVERED	WARM UP / DRILLS

WHAT I HAVE LEARNED	POINTS FOR IMPROVEMENT

NOTES

SKILLS COMPLETED
WRITE DOWN THE SKILLS YOU WORKED ON AND DEVELOPED DURING YOUR CLASS

SKILLS TO IMPROVE
WRITE DOWN AREAS THAT YOU CAN IMPROVE ON FOR YOUR NEXT TRAINING SESSION

INSTRUCTOR FEEDBACK
WRITE DOWN IF YOUR INSTRUCTOR HAS A SKILL, TECHNIQUE, OR COMBINATION FOR YOU TO FOCUS ON

EXTRA NOTES
DO YOU HAVE EXTRA NOTES OR THOUGHTS YOU WOULD LIKE TO WRITE DOWN?

JOURNAL

JOURNAL

MY SESSION

DATE		WEEK		SESSION	
BELT		INSTRUCTOR			

MY GOALS OF THE DAY

☐

☐

☐

☐

☐

TRAINING PARTNERS

☐	☐
☐	☐
☐	☐

TECHNIQUES COVERED / WARM UP / DRILLS

TECHNIQUES COVERED	WARM UP / DRILLS

WHAT I HAVE LEARNED / POINTS FOR IMPROVEMENT

WHAT I HAVE LEARNED	POINTS FOR IMPROVEMENT

NOTES

SKILLS COMPLETED
WRITE DOWN THE SKILLS YOU WORKED ON AND DEVELOPED DURING YOUR CLASS

SKILLS TO IMPROVE
WRITE DOWN AREAS THAT YOU CAN IMPROVE ON FOR YOUR NEXT TRAINING SESSION

INSTRUCTOR FEEDBACK
WRITE DOWN IF YOUR INSTRUCTOR HAS A SKILL, TECHNIQUE, OR COMBINATION FOR YOU TO FOCUS ON

EXTRA NOTES
DO YOU HAVE EXTRA NOTES OR THOUGHTS YOU WOULD LIKE TO WRITE DOWN?

JOURNAL

JOURNAL

MY SESSION

DATE		WEEK		SESSION	
BELT		INSTRUCTOR			

MY GOALS OF THE DAY

- ☐
- ☐
- ☐
- ☐
- ☐

TRAINING PARTNERS

☐	☐
☐	☐
☐	☐

TECHNIQUES COVERED	WARM UP / DRILLS

WHAT I HAVE LEARNED	POINTS FOR IMPROVEMENT

NOTES

SKILLS COMPLETED
WRITE DOWN THE SKILLS YOU WORKED ON AND DEVELOPED DURING YOUR CLASS

SKILLS TO IMPROVE
WRITE DOWN AREAS THAT YOU CAN IMPROVE ON FOR YOUR NEXT TRAINING SESSION

INSTRUCTOR FEEDBACK
WRITE DOWN IF YOUR INSTRUCTOR HAS A SKILL, TECHNIQUE, OR COMBINATION FOR YOU TO FOCUS ON

EXTRA NOTES
DO YOU HAVE EXTRA NOTES OR THOUGHTS YOU WOULD LIKE TO WRITE DOWN?

JOURNAL

JOURNAL

MY SESSION

DATE		WEEK		SESSION	
BELT		INSTRUCTOR			

MY GOALS OF THE DAY

- ☐
- ☐
- ☐
- ☐
- ☐

TRAINING PARTNERS

☐	☐
☐	☐
☐	☐

TECHNIQUES COVERED	WARM UP / DRILLS

WHAT I HAVE LEARNED	POINTS FOR IMPROVEMENT

NOTES

ILLS COMPLETED
ITE DOWN THE SKILLS YOU WORKED ON AND DEVELOPED DURING YOUR CLASS

KILLS TO IMPROVE
RITE DOWN AREAS THAT YOU CAN IMPROVE ON FOR YOUR NEXT TRAINING SESSION

NSTRUCTOR FEEDBACK
WRITE DOWN IF YOUR INSTRUCTOR HAS A SKILL, TECHNIQUE, OR COMBINATION FOR YOU TO FOCUS ON

EXTRA NOTES
DO YOU HAVE EXTRA NOTES OR THOUGHTS YOU WOULD LIKE TO WRITE DOWN?

JOURNAL

JOURNAL

MY SESSION

DATE		WEEK		SESSION	
BELT		INSTRUCTOR			

MY GOALS OF THE DAY

- ☐
- ☐
- ☐
- ☐
- ☐

TRAINING PARTNERS

☐	☐
☐	☐
☐	☐

TECHNIQUES COVERED	WARM UP / DRILLS

WHAT I HAVE LEARNED	POINTS FOR IMPROVEMENT

NOTES

SKILLS COMPLETED
WRITE DOWN THE SKILLS YOU WORKED ON AND DEVELOPED DURING YOUR CLASS

SKILLS TO IMPROVE
WRITE DOWN AREAS THAT YOU CAN IMPROVE ON FOR YOUR NEXT TRAINING SESSION

INSTRUCTOR FEEDBACK
WRITE DOWN IF YOUR INSTRUCTOR HAS A SKILL, TECHNIQUE, OR COMBINATION FOR YOU TO FOCUS ON

EXTRA NOTES
DO YOU HAVE EXTRA NOTES OR THOUGHTS YOU WOULD LIKE TO WRITE DOWN?

JOURNAL

JOURNAL

MY SESSION

DATE		WEEK		SESSION	
BELT		INSTRUCTOR			

MY GOALS OF THE DAY

- ☐
- ☐
- ☐
- ☐
- ☐

TRAINING PARTNERS

☐	☐
☐	☐
☐	☐

TECHNIQUES COVERED	WARM UP / DRILLS

WHAT I HAVE LEARNED	POINTS FOR IMPROVEMENT

NOTES

SKILLS COMPLETED
WRITE DOWN THE SKILLS YOU WORKED ON AND DEVELOPED DURING YOUR CLASS

SKILLS TO IMPROVE
WRITE DOWN AREAS THAT YOU CAN IMPROVE ON FOR YOUR NEXT TRAINING SESSION

INSTRUCTOR FEEDBACK
WRITE DOWN IF YOUR INSTRUCTOR HAS A SKILL, TECHNIQUE, OR COMBINATION FOR YOU TO FOCUS ON

EXTRA NOTES
DO YOU HAVE EXTRA NOTES OR THOUGHTS YOU WOULD LIKE TO WRITE DOWN?

JOURNAL

JOURNAL

MY SESSION

DATE		WEEK		SESSION	
BELT		INSTRUCTOR			

MY GOALS OF THE DAY

- ☐
- ☐
- ☐
- ☐
- ☐

TRAINING PARTNERS

☐	☐
☐	☐
☐	☐

TECHNIQUES COVERED	WARM UP / DRILLS

WHAT I HAVE LEARNED	POINTS FOR IMPROVEMENT

NOTES

ILLS COMPLETED
TE DOWN THE SKILLS YOU WORKED ON AND DEVELOPED DURING YOUR CLASS

KILLS TO IMPROVE
RITE DOWN AREAS THAT YOU CAN IMPROVE ON FOR YOUR NEXT TRAINING SESSION

NSTRUCTOR FEEDBACK
RITE DOWN IF YOUR INSTRUCTOR HAS A SKILL, TECHNIQUE, OR COMBINATION FOR YOU TO FOCUS ON

EXTRA NOTES
DO YOU HAVE EXTRA NOTES OR THOUGHTS YOU WOULD LIKE TO WRITE DOWN?

JOURNAL

JOURNAL

MY SESSION

DATE		WEEK		SESSION	
BELT		INSTRUCTOR			

MY GOALS OF THE DAY

- ☐
- ☐
- ☐
- ☐
- ☐

TRAINING PARTNERS

☐	☐
☐	☐
☐	☐

TECHNIQUES COVERED	WARM UP / DRILLS

WHAT I HAVE LEARNED	POINTS FOR IMPROVEMENT

NOTES

SKILLS COMPLETED
WRITE DOWN THE SKILLS YOU WORKED ON AND DEVELOPED DURING YOUR CLASS

SKILLS TO IMPROVE
WRITE DOWN AREAS THAT YOU CAN IMPROVE ON FOR YOUR NEXT TRAINING SESSION

INSTRUCTOR FEEDBACK
WRITE DOWN IF YOUR INSTRUCTOR HAS A SKILL, TECHNIQUE, OR COMBINATION FOR YOU TO FOCUS ON

EXTRA NOTES
DO YOU HAVE EXTRA NOTES OR THOUGHTS YOU WOULD LIKE TO WRITE DOWN?

JOURNAL

JOURNAL

MY SESSION

DATE		WEEK		SESSION	
BELT		INSTRUCTOR			

MY GOALS OF THE DAY

- ☐
- ☐
- ☐
- ☐
- ☐

TRAINING PARTNERS

☐	☐
☐	☐
☐	☐

TECHNIQUES COVERED	WARM UP / DRILLS

WHAT I HAVE LEARNED	POINTS FOR IMPROVEMENT

NOTES

SKILLS COMPLETED
WRITE DOWN THE SKILLS YOU WORKED ON AND DEVELOPED DURING YOUR CLASS

SKILLS TO IMPROVE
WRITE DOWN AREAS THAT YOU CAN IMPROVE ON FOR YOUR NEXT TRAINING SESSION

INSTRUCTOR FEEDBACK
WRITE DOWN IF YOUR INSTRUCTOR HAS A SKILL, TECHNIQUE, OR COMBINATION FOR YOU TO FOCUS ON

EXTRA NOTES
DO YOU HAVE EXTRA NOTES OR THOUGHTS YOU WOULD LIKE TO WRITE DOWN?

JOURNAL

JOURNAL

MY SESSION

DATE		WEEK		SESSION	
BELT		INSTRUCTOR			

MY GOALS OF THE DAY

- ☐
- ☐
- ☐
- ☐
- ☐

TRAINING PARTNERS

☐	☐
☐	☐
☐	☐

TECHNIQUES COVERED	WARM UP / DRILLS

WHAT I HAVE LEARNED	POINTS FOR IMPROVEMENT

NOTES

SKILLS COMPLETED
WRITE DOWN THE SKILLS YOU WORKED ON AND DEVELOPED DURING YOUR CLASS

SKILLS TO IMPROVE
WRITE DOWN AREAS THAT YOU CAN IMPROVE ON FOR YOUR NEXT TRAINING SESSION

INSTRUCTOR FEEDBACK
WRITE DOWN IF YOUR INSTRUCTOR HAS A SKILL, TECHNIQUE, OR COMBINATION FOR YOU TO FOCUS ON

EXTRA NOTES
DO YOU HAVE EXTRA NOTES OR THOUGHTS YOU WOULD LIKE TO WRITE DOWN?

JOURNAL

JOURNAL

MY SESSION

DATE		WEEK		SESSION	
BELT		INSTRUCTOR			

MY GOALS OF THE DAY

- ☐
- ☐
- ☐
- ☐
- ☐

TRAINING PARTNERS

☐	☐
☐	☐
☐	☐

TECHNIQUES COVERED	WARM UP / DRILLS

WHAT I HAVE LEARNED	POINTS FOR IMPROVEMENT

NOTES

SKILLS COMPLETED
WRITE DOWN THE SKILLS YOU WORKED ON AND DEVELOPED DURING YOUR CLASS

SKILLS TO IMPROVE
WRITE DOWN AREAS THAT YOU CAN IMPROVE ON FOR YOUR NEXT TRAINING SESSION

INSTRUCTOR FEEDBACK
WRITE DOWN IF YOUR INSTRUCTOR HAS A SKILL, TECHNIQUE, OR COMBINATION FOR YOU TO FOCUS ON

EXTRA NOTES
DO YOU HAVE EXTRA NOTES OR THOUGHTS YOU WOULD LIKE TO WRITE DOWN?

JOURNAL

JOURNAL

MY SESSION

DATE		WEEK		SESSION	
BELT		INSTRUCTOR			

MY GOALS OF THE DAY

- ☐
- ☐
- ☐
- ☐
- ☐

TRAINING PARTNERS

☐	☐
☐	☐
☐	☐

TECHNIQUES COVERED	WARM UP / DRILLS

WHAT I HAVE LEARNED	POINTS FOR IMPROVEMENT

NOTES

SKILLS COMPLETED
WRITE DOWN THE SKILLS YOU WORKED ON AND DEVELOPED DURING YOUR CLASS

SKILLS TO IMPROVE
WRITE DOWN AREAS THAT YOU CAN IMPROVE ON FOR YOUR NEXT TRAINING SESSION

INSTRUCTOR FEEDBACK
WRITE DOWN IF YOUR INSTRUCTOR HAS A SKILL, TECHNIQUE, OR COMBINATION FOR YOU TO FOCUS ON

EXTRA NOTES
DO YOU HAVE EXTRA NOTES OR THOUGHTS YOU WOULD LIKE TO WRITE DOWN?

JOURNAL

JOURNAL

MY SESSION

DATE		WEEK		SESSION	
BELT		INSTRUCTOR			

MY GOALS OF THE DAY

- ☐
- ☐
- ☐
- ☐
- ☐

TRAINING PARTNERS

☐	☐
☐	☐
☐	☐

TECHNIQUES COVERED	WARM UP / DRILLS

WHAT I HAVE LEARNED	POINTS FOR IMPROVEMENT

NOTES

ILLS COMPLETED
TE DOWN THE SKILLS YOU WORKED ON AND DEVELOPED DURING YOUR CLASS

ILLS TO IMPROVE
RITE DOWN AREAS THAT YOU CAN IMPROVE ON FOR YOUR NEXT TRAINING SESSION

ISTRUCTOR FEEDBACK
RITE DOWN IF YOUR INSTRUCTOR HAS A SKILL, TECHNIQUE, OR COMBINATION FOR YOU TO FOCUS ON

XTRA NOTES
O YOU HAVE EXTRA NOTES OR THOUGHTS YOU WOULD LIKE TO WRITE DOWN?

JOURNAL

JOURNAL

MY SESSION

DATE		WEEK		SESSION	
BELT		INSTRUCTOR			

MY GOALS OF THE DAY

- ☐
- ☐
- ☐
- ☐
- ☐

TRAINING PARTNERS

☐	☐
☐	☐
☐	☐

TECHNIQUES COVERED	WARM UP / DRILLS

WHAT I HAVE LEARNED	POINTS FOR IMPROVEMENT

NOTES

SKILLS COMPLETED
WRITE DOWN THE SKILLS YOU WORKED ON AND DEVELOPED DURING YOUR CLASS

SKILLS TO IMPROVE
WRITE DOWN AREAS THAT YOU CAN IMPROVE ON FOR YOUR NEXT TRAINING SESSION

INSTRUCTOR FEEDBACK
WRITE DOWN IF YOUR INSTRUCTOR HAS A SKILL, TECHNIQUE, OR COMBINATION FOR YOU TO FOCUS ON

EXTRA NOTES
DO YOU HAVE EXTRA NOTES OR THOUGHTS YOU WOULD LIKE TO WRITE DOWN?

JOURNAL

JOURNAL

MY SESSION

DATE		WEEK		SESSION	
BELT		INSTRUCTOR			

MY GOALS OF THE DAY

☐

☐

☐

☐

☐

TRAINING PARTNERS

☐   ☐

☐   ☐

☐   ☐

TECHNIQUES COVERED	WARM UP / DRILLS

WHAT I HAVE LEARNED	POINTS FOR IMPROVEMENT

NOTES

SKILLS COMPLETED
WRITE DOWN THE SKILLS YOU WORKED ON AND DEVELOPED DURING YOUR CLASS

SKILLS TO IMPROVE
WRITE DOWN AREAS THAT YOU CAN IMPROVE ON FOR YOUR NEXT TRAINING SESSION

INSTRUCTOR FEEDBACK
WRITE DOWN IF YOUR INSTRUCTOR HAS A SKILL, TECHNIQUE, OR COMBINATION FOR YOU TO FOCUS ON

EXTRA NOTES
DO YOU HAVE EXTRA NOTES OR THOUGHTS YOU WOULD LIKE TO WRITE DOWN?

JOURNAL

JOURNAL

MY SESSION

DATE		WEEK		SESSION	
BELT		INSTRUCTOR			

MY GOALS OF THE DAY

- ☐
- ☐
- ☐
- ☐
- ☐

TRAINING PARTNERS

☐	☐
☐	☐
☐	☐

TECHNIQUES COVERED	WARM UP / DRILLS

WHAT I HAVE LEARNED	POINTS FOR IMPROVEMENT

NOTES

ILLS COMPLETED
TE DOWN THE SKILLS YOU WORKED ON AND DEVELOPED DURING YOUR CLASS

ILLS TO IMPROVE
ITE DOWN AREAS THAT YOU CAN IMPROVE ON FOR YOUR NEXT TRAINING SESSION

ISTRUCTOR FEEDBACK
RITE DOWN IF YOUR INSTRUCTOR HAS A SKILL, TECHNIQUE, OR COMBINATION FOR YOU TO FOCUS ON

XTRA NOTES
O YOU HAVE EXTRA NOTES OR THOUGHTS YOU WOULD LIKE TO WRITE DOWN?

JOURNAL

JOURNAL

MY SESSION

DATE		WEEK		SESSION	
BELT		INSTRUCTOR			

MY GOALS OF THE DAY

☐

☐

☐

☐

☐

TRAINING PARTNERS

☐	☐
☐	☐
☐	☐

TECHNIQUES COVERED	WARM UP / DRILLS

WHAT I HAVE LEARNED	POINTS FOR IMPROVEMENT

NOTES

SKILLS COMPLETED
WRITE DOWN THE SKILLS YOU WORKED ON AND DEVELOPED DURING YOUR CLASS

SKILLS TO IMPROVE
WRITE DOWN AREAS THAT YOU CAN IMPROVE ON FOR YOUR NEXT TRAINING SESSION

INSTRUCTOR FEEDBACK
WRITE DOWN IF YOUR INSTRUCTOR HAS A SKILL, TECHNIQUE, OR COMBINATION FOR YOU TO FOCUS ON

EXTRA NOTES
DO YOU HAVE EXTRA NOTES OR THOUGHTS YOU WOULD LIKE TO WRITE DOWN?

JOURNAL

JOURNAL

MY SESSION

DATE		WEEK		SESSION	
BELT		INSTRUCTOR			

MY GOALS OF THE DAY

☐

☐

☐

☐

☐

TRAINING PARTNERS

☐	☐
☐	☐
☐	☐

TECHNIQUES COVERED	WARM UP / DRILLS

WHAT I HAVE LEARNED	POINTS FOR IMPROVEMENT

NOTES

SKILLS COMPLETED
WRITE DOWN THE SKILLS YOU WORKED ON AND DEVELOPED DURING YOUR CLASS

SKILLS TO IMPROVE
WRITE DOWN AREAS THAT YOU CAN IMPROVE ON FOR YOUR NEXT TRAINING SESSION

INSTRUCTOR FEEDBACK
WRITE DOWN IF YOUR INSTRUCTOR HAS A SKILL, TECHNIQUE, OR COMBINATION FOR YOU TO FOCUS ON

EXTRA NOTES
DO YOU HAVE EXTRA NOTES OR THOUGHTS YOU WOULD LIKE TO WRITE DOWN?

JOURNAL

JOURNAL

MY SESSION

DATE		WEEK		SESSION	
BELT		INSTRUCTOR			

MY GOALS OF THE DAY

- ☐
- ☐
- ☐
- ☐
- ☐

TRAINING PARTNERS

☐	☐
☐	☐
☐	☐

TECHNIQUES COVERED	WARM UP / DRILLS

WHAT I HAVE LEARNED	POINTS FOR IMPROVEMENT

NOTES

SKILLS COMPLETED
WRITE DOWN THE SKILLS YOU WORKED ON AND DEVELOPED DURING YOUR CLASS

SKILLS TO IMPROVE
WRITE DOWN AREAS THAT YOU CAN IMPROVE ON FOR YOUR NEXT TRAINING SESSION

INSTRUCTOR FEEDBACK
WRITE DOWN IF YOUR INSTRUCTOR HAS A SKILL, TECHNIQUE, OR COMBINATION FOR YOU TO FOCUS ON

EXTRA NOTES
DO YOU HAVE EXTRA NOTES OR THOUGHTS YOU WOULD LIKE TO WRITE DOWN?

JOURNAL

JOURNAL

MY SESSION

DATE		WEEK		SESSION	
BELT		INSTRUCTOR			

MY GOALS OF THE DAY

- ☐
- ☐
- ☐
- ☐
- ☐

TRAINING PARTNERS

☐	☐
☐	☐
☐	☐

TECHNIQUES COVERED	WARM UP / DRILLS

WHAT I HAVE LEARNED	POINTS FOR IMPROVEMENT

NOTES

KILLS COMPLETED
WRITE DOWN THE SKILLS YOU WORKED ON AND DEVELOPED DURING YOUR CLASS

SKILLS TO IMPROVE
WRITE DOWN AREAS THAT YOU CAN IMPROVE ON FOR YOUR NEXT TRAINING SESSION

INSTRUCTOR FEEDBACK
WRITE DOWN IF YOUR INSTRUCTOR HAS A SKILL, TECHNIQUE, OR COMBINATION FOR YOU TO FOCUS ON

EXTRA NOTES
DO YOU HAVE EXTRA NOTES OR THOUGHTS YOU WOULD LIKE TO WRITE DOWN?

JOURNAL

JOURNAL

MY SESSION

DATE		WEEK		SESSION	
BELT		INSTRUCTOR			

MY GOALS OF THE DAY

☐

☐

☐

☐

☐

TRAINING PARTNERS

☐	☐
☐	☐
☐	☐

TECHNIQUES COVERED | WARM UP / DRILLS

WHAT I HAVE LEARNED | POINTS FOR IMPROVEMENT

NOTES

SKILLS COMPLETED
WRITE DOWN THE SKILLS YOU WORKED ON AND DEVELOPED DURING YOUR CLASS

SKILLS TO IMPROVE
WRITE DOWN AREAS THAT YOU CAN IMPROVE ON FOR YOUR NEXT TRAINING SESSION

INSTRUCTOR FEEDBACK
WRITE DOWN IF YOUR INSTRUCTOR HAS A SKILL, TECHNIQUE, OR COMBINATION FOR YOU TO FOCUS ON

EXTRA NOTES
DO YOU HAVE EXTRA NOTES OR THOUGHTS YOU WOULD LIKE TO WRITE DOWN?

JOURNAL

JOURNAL

MY SESSION

DATE		WEEK		SESSION	
BELT		INSTRUCTOR			

MY GOALS OF THE DAY

- ☐
- ☐
- ☐
- ☐
- ☐

TRAINING PARTNERS

☐	☐
☐	☐
☐	☐

TECHNIQUES COVERED	WARM UP / DRILLS

WHAT I HAVE LEARNED	POINTS FOR IMPROVEMENT

NOTES

LLS COMPLETED
TE DOWN THE SKILLS YOU WORKED ON AND DEVELOPED DURING YOUR CLASS

ILLS TO IMPROVE
ITE DOWN AREAS THAT YOU CAN IMPROVE ON FOR YOUR NEXT TRAINING SESSION

STRUCTOR FEEDBACK
RITE DOWN IF YOUR INSTRUCTOR HAS A SKILL, TECHNIQUE, OR COMBINATION FOR YOU TO FOCUS ON

XTRA NOTES
O YOU HAVE EXTRA NOTES OR THOUGHTS YOU WOULD LIKE TO WRITE DOWN?

JOURNAL

JOURNAL

MY SESSION

DATE		WEEK		SESSION	
BELT		INSTRUCTOR			

MY GOALS OF THE DAY

- ☐
- ☐
- ☐
- ☐
- ☐

TRAINING PARTNERS

☐	☐
☐	☐
☐	☐

TECHNIQUES COVERED	WARM UP / DRILLS

WHAT I HAVE LEARNED	POINTS FOR IMPROVEMENT

NOTES

SKILLS COMPLETED
WRITE DOWN THE SKILLS YOU WORKED ON AND DEVELOPED DURING YOUR CLASS

SKILLS TO IMPROVE
WRITE DOWN AREAS THAT YOU CAN IMPROVE ON FOR YOUR NEXT TRAINING SESSION

INSTRUCTOR FEEDBACK
WRITE DOWN IF YOUR INSTRUCTOR HAS A SKILL, TECHNIQUE, OR COMBINATION FOR YOU TO FOCUS ON

EXTRA NOTES
DO YOU HAVE EXTRA NOTES OR THOUGHTS YOU WOULD LIKE TO WRITE DOWN?

JOURNAL

JOURNAL

MY SESSION

DATE		WEEK		SESSION	
BELT		INSTRUCTOR			

MY GOALS OF THE DAY

- ☐
- ☐
- ☐
- ☐
- ☐

TRAINING PARTNERS

☐	☐
☐	☐
☐	☐

TECHNIQUES COVERED	WARM UP / DRILLS

WHAT I HAVE LEARNED	POINTS FOR IMPROVEMENT

NOTES

SKILLS COMPLETED
WRITE DOWN THE SKILLS YOU WORKED ON AND DEVELOPED DURING YOUR CLASS

SKILLS TO IMPROVE
WRITE DOWN AREAS THAT YOU CAN IMPROVE ON FOR YOUR NEXT TRAINING SESSION

INSTRUCTOR FEEDBACK
WRITE DOWN IF YOUR INSTRUCTOR HAS A SKILL, TECHNIQUE, OR COMBINATION FOR YOU TO FOCUS ON

EXTRA NOTES
DO YOU HAVE EXTRA NOTES OR THOUGHTS YOU WOULD LIKE TO WRITE DOWN?

JOURNAL

JOURNAL

MY SESSION

DATE		WEEK		SESSION	
BELT		INSTRUCTOR			

MY GOALS OF THE DAY

- ☐
- ☐
- ☐
- ☐
- ☐

TRAINING PARTNERS

☐	☐
☐	☐
☐	☐

TECHNIQUES COVERED	WARM UP / DRILLS

WHAT I HAVE LEARNED	POINTS FOR IMPROVEMENT

NOTES

LLS COMPLETED
TE DOWN THE SKILLS YOU WORKED ON AND DEVELOPED DURING YOUR CLASS

ILLS TO IMPROVE
TE DOWN AREAS THAT YOU CAN IMPROVE ON FOR YOUR NEXT TRAINING SESSION

STRUCTOR FEEDBACK
RITE DOWN IF YOUR INSTRUCTOR HAS A SKILL, TECHNIQUE, OR COMBINATION FOR YOU TO FOCUS ON

XTRA NOTES
) YOU HAVE EXTRA NOTES OR THOUGHTS YOU WOULD LIKE TO WRITE DOWN?

JOURNAL

JOURNAL

MY SESSION

DATE		WEEK		SESSION	
BELT		INSTRUCTOR			

MY GOALS OF THE DAY

- ☐
- ☐
- ☐
- ☐
- ☐

TRAINING PARTNERS

☐	☐
☐	☐
☐	☐

TECHNIQUES COVERED	WARM UP / DRILLS

WHAT I HAVE LEARNED	POINTS FOR IMPROVEMENT

NOTES

SKILLS COMPLETED
WRITE DOWN THE SKILLS YOU WORKED ON AND DEVELOPED DURING YOUR CLASS

SKILLS TO IMPROVE
WRITE DOWN AREAS THAT YOU CAN IMPROVE ON FOR YOUR NEXT TRAINING SESSION

INSTRUCTOR FEEDBACK
WRITE DOWN IF YOUR INSTRUCTOR HAS A SKILL, TECHNIQUE, OR COMBINATION FOR YOU TO FOCUS ON

EXTRA NOTES
DO YOU HAVE EXTRA NOTES OR THOUGHTS YOU WOULD LIKE TO WRITE DOWN?

JOURNAL

JOURNAL

MY SESSION

DATE		WEEK		SESSION	
BELT		INSTRUCTOR			

MY GOALS OF THE DAY

- ☐
- ☐
- ☐
- ☐
- ☐

TRAINING PARTNERS

☐	☐
☐	☐
☐	☐

TECHNIQUES COVERED	WARM UP / DRILLS

WHAT I HAVE LEARNED	POINTS FOR IMPROVEMENT

NOTES

SKILLS COMPLETED
WRITE DOWN THE SKILLS YOU WORKED ON AND DEVELOPED DURING YOUR CLASS

SKILLS TO IMPROVE
WRITE DOWN AREAS THAT YOU CAN IMPROVE ON FOR YOUR NEXT TRAINING SESSION

INSTRUCTOR FEEDBACK
WRITE DOWN IF YOUR INSTRUCTOR HAS A SKILL, TECHNIQUE, OR COMBINATION FOR YOU TO FOCUS ON

EXTRA NOTES
DO YOU HAVE EXTRA NOTES OR THOUGHTS YOU WOULD LIKE TO WRITE DOWN?

JOURNAL

JOURNAL

MY SESSION

DATE		WEEK		SESSION	
BELT		INSTRUCTOR			

MY GOALS OF THE DAY

- ☐
- ☐
- ☐
- ☐
- ☐

TRAINING PARTNERS

☐	☐
☐	☐
☐	☐

TECHNIQUES COVERED	WARM UP / DRILLS

WHAT I HAVE LEARNED	POINTS FOR IMPROVEMENT

NOTES

SKILLS COMPLETED
WRITE DOWN THE SKILLS YOU WORKED ON AND DEVELOPED DURING YOUR CLASS

SKILLS TO IMPROVE
WRITE DOWN AREAS THAT YOU CAN IMPROVE ON FOR YOUR NEXT TRAINING SESSION

INSTRUCTOR FEEDBACK
WRITE DOWN IF YOUR INSTRUCTOR HAS A SKILL, TECHNIQUE, OR COMBINATION FOR YOU TO FOCUS ON

EXTRA NOTES
DO YOU HAVE EXTRA NOTES OR THOUGHTS YOU WOULD LIKE TO WRITE DOWN?

JOURNAL

JOURNAL

MY SESSION

DATE		WEEK		SESSION	
BELT		INSTRUCTOR			

MY GOALS OF THE DAY

- ☐
- ☐
- ☐
- ☐
- ☐

TRAINING PARTNERS

☐	☐
☐	☐
☐	☐

TECHNIQUES COVERED	WARM UP / DRILLS

WHAT I HAVE LEARNED	POINTS FOR IMPROVEMENT

NOTES

SKILLS COMPLETED
WRITE DOWN THE SKILLS YOU WORKED ON AND DEVELOPED DURING YOUR CLASS

SKILLS TO IMPROVE
WRITE DOWN AREAS THAT YOU CAN IMPROVE ON FOR YOUR NEXT TRAINING SESSION

INSTRUCTOR FEEDBACK
WRITE DOWN IF YOUR INSTRUCTOR HAS A SKILL, TECHNIQUE, OR COMBINATION FOR YOU TO FOCUS ON

EXTRA NOTES
DO YOU HAVE EXTRA NOTES OR THOUGHTS YOU WOULD LIKE TO WRITE DOWN?

JOURNAL

JOURNAL

MY SESSION

DATE		WEEK		SESSION	
BELT		INSTRUCTOR			

MY GOALS OF THE DAY

☐

☐

☐

☐

☐

TRAINING PARTNERS

☐   ☐

☐   ☐

☐   ☐

TECHNIQUES COVERED	WARM UP / DRILLS

WHAT I HAVE LEARNED	POINTS FOR IMPROVEMENT

NOTES

SKILLS COMPLETED
WRITE DOWN THE SKILLS YOU WORKED ON AND DEVELOPED DURING YOUR CLASS

SKILLS TO IMPROVE
WRITE DOWN AREAS THAT YOU CAN IMPROVE ON FOR YOUR NEXT TRAINING SESSION

INSTRUCTOR FEEDBACK
WRITE DOWN IF YOUR INSTRUCTOR HAS A SKILL, TECHNIQUE, OR COMBINATION FOR YOU TO FOCUS ON

EXTRA NOTES
DO YOU HAVE EXTRA NOTES OR THOUGHTS YOU WOULD LIKE TO WRITE DOWN?

JOURNAL

JOURNAL

MY SESSION

DATE		WEEK		SESSION	
BELT		INSTRUCTOR			

MY GOALS OF THE DAY

- ☐
- ☐
- ☐
- ☐
- ☐

TRAINING PARTNERS

☐	☐
☐	☐
☐	☐

TECHNIQUES COVERED	WARM UP / DRILLS

WHAT I HAVE LEARNED	POINTS FOR IMPROVEMENT

NOTES

LLS COMPLETED
E DOWN THE SKILLS YOU WORKED ON AND DEVELOPED DURING YOUR CLASS

LLS TO IMPROVE
TE DOWN AREAS THAT YOU CAN IMPROVE ON FOR YOUR NEXT TRAINING SESSION

STRUCTOR FEEDBACK
TE DOWN IF YOUR INSTRUCTOR HAS A SKILL, TECHNIQUE, OR COMBINATION FOR YOU TO FOCUS ON

XTRA NOTES
YOU HAVE EXTRA NOTES OR THOUGHTS YOU WOULD LIKE TO WRITE DOWN?

JOURNAL

JOURNAL

MY SESSION

DATE		WEEK		SESSION	
BELT		INSTRUCTOR			

MY GOALS OF THE DAY

- ☐
- ☐
- ☐
- ☐
- ☐

TRAINING PARTNERS

☐	☐
☐	☐
☐	☐

TECHNIQUES COVERED	WARM UP / DRILLS

WHAT I HAVE LEARNED	POINTS FOR IMPROVEMENT

NOTES

SKILLS COMPLETED
WRITE DOWN THE SKILLS YOU WORKED ON AND DEVELOPED DURING YOUR CLASS

SKILLS TO IMPROVE
WRITE DOWN AREAS THAT YOU CAN IMPROVE ON FOR YOUR NEXT TRAINING SESSION

INSTRUCTOR FEEDBACK
WRITE DOWN IF YOUR INSTRUCTOR HAS A SKILL, TECHNIQUE, OR COMBINATION FOR YOU TO FOCUS ON

EXTRA NOTES
DO YOU HAVE EXTRA NOTES OR THOUGHTS YOU WOULD LIKE TO WRITE DOWN?

JOURNAL

JOURNAL

MY SESSION

DATE		WEEK		SESSION	
BELT		INSTRUCTOR			

MY GOALS OF THE DAY

- ☐
- ☐
- ☐
- ☐
- ☐

TRAINING PARTNERS

☐		☐	
☐		☐	
☐		☐	

TECHNIQUES COVERED	WARM UP / DRILLS

WHAT I HAVE LEARNED	POINTS FOR IMPROVEMENT

NOTES

SKILLS COMPLETED
WRITE DOWN THE SKILLS YOU WORKED ON AND DEVELOPED DURING YOUR CLASS

SKILLS TO IMPROVE
WRITE DOWN AREAS THAT YOU CAN IMPROVE ON FOR YOUR NEXT TRAINING SESSION

INSTRUCTOR FEEDBACK
WRITE DOWN IF YOUR INSTRUCTOR HAS A SKILL, TECHNIQUE, OR COMBINATION FOR YOU TO FOCUS ON

EXTRA NOTES
DO YOU HAVE EXTRA NOTES OR THOUGHTS YOU WOULD LIKE TO WRITE DOWN?

JOURNAL

JOURNAL

MY SESSION

DATE		WEEK		SESSION	
BELT		INSTRUCTOR			

MY GOALS OF THE DAY

- ☐
- ☐
- ☐
- ☐
- ☐

TRAINING PARTNERS

☐	☐
☐	☐
☐	☐

TECHNIQUES COVERED	WARM UP / DRILLS

WHAT I HAVE LEARNED	POINTS FOR IMPROVEMENT

NOTES

LLS COMPLETED
E DOWN THE SKILLS YOU WORKED ON AND DEVELOPED DURING YOUR CLASS

LLS TO IMPROVE
TE DOWN AREAS THAT YOU CAN IMPROVE ON FOR YOUR NEXT TRAINING SESSION

STRUCTOR FEEDBACK
TE DOWN IF YOUR INSTRUCTOR HAS A SKILL, TECHNIQUE, OR COMBINATION FOR YOU TO FOCUS ON

XTRA NOTES
YOU HAVE EXTRA NOTES OR THOUGHTS YOU WOULD LIKE TO WRITE DOWN?

JOURNAL

JOURNAL

Made in the USA
Monee, IL
03 May 2023